11+ tests

11+
Maths
Success

Age 7-8

Age 8-9

Age 9-10

Age 10-11

10-Minute Tests

Jason White, Val Mitchell and Sally Moon

Sample page

clear instructional text

test number and topic being covered

section number for quick reference

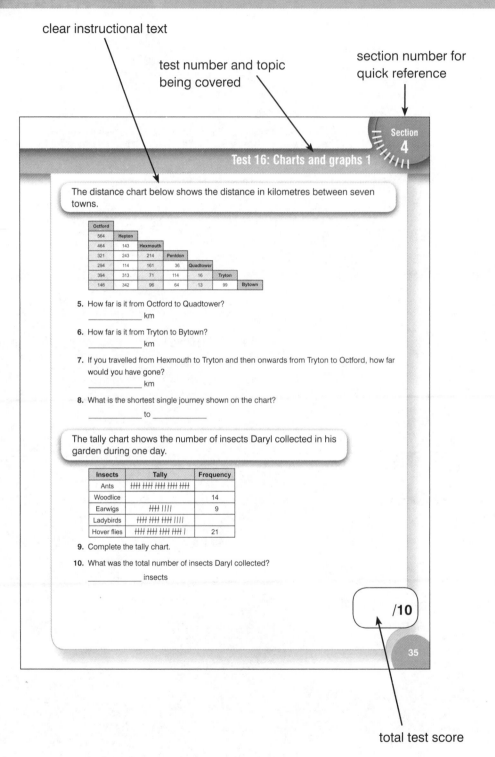

The distance chart below shows the distance in kilometres between seven towns.

Octford						
564	Hepton					
464	143	Hexmouth				
321	243	214	Pentdon			
294	114	161	36	Quadtower		
394	313	71	114	16	Tryton	
146	342	96	64	13	99	Bytown

5. How far is it from Octford to Quadtower?

_____ km

6. How far is it from Tryton to Bytown?

_____ km

7. If you travelled from Hexmouth to Tryton and then onwards from Tryton to Octford, how far would you have gone?

_____ km

8. What is the shortest single journey shown on the chart?

_____ to _____

The tally chart shows the number of insects Daryl collected in his garden during one day.

Insects	Tally	Frequency
Ants	||| |||| |||| |||| ||||	
Woodlice		14
Earwigs	|||| ||||	9
Ladybirds	|||| |||| |||| ||||	
Hover flies	|||| |||| |||| ||||		21

9. Complete the tally chart.

10. What was the total number of insects Daryl collected?

_____ insects

/10

35

total test score

2

Contents

Test 1: Ordering and rounding whole numbers 1

1. Put a circle around the **largest** number below.

   10358   10538   10835   10700   10799

2. Write the value of the digit in bold in each number in words.

   a) 1**2**89 _____

   b) 1**2**289 _____

   c) 1**2**8952 _____

3. Put these numbers in order, starting with the **smallest**.

   a) 2851   2185   3518   1825   1852

   b) 6430   6515   7000   6001   6099

4. Put these numbers in order, starting with the **largest**.

   a) 10380   10019   9984   11111   10307

   b) 40440   40019   49984   5987   40621

5. Put these numbers in order, starting with the **largest**.

   a) -20   -19   19   190   0

   b) 40440   40019   -49984   -5987   40621

6. Circle the number that is **nearest to 1000**.

   -120   4920   2210   2516   9999

7. Circle the number that is **nearest to 10000**.

   1999864   8970   3500   350500   11120

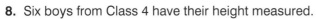
8. Six boys from Class 4 have their height measured.

| Jon | Eric | Ahmed | Jake | Nathan | Billy |
| 138cm | 119cm | 140cm | 109cm | 120cm | 141cm |

a) Who is the tallest boy? _____

b) Who is the second smallest boy? _____

c) Who is the third tallest boy? _____

9. The temperature was measured in various places in the UK:

A Nottingham -8°C **B** Macclesfield -6°C **C** Carlisle -14°C

D London 1°C **E** Brighton 8°C

a) Put these temperatures in order, starting with the lowest, using the letter that represents each one. _____

b) What is the difference between the two lowest temperatures? _____ °C

c) If the temperature in Macclesfield rose by 7°C, what would the new temperature be?
_____ °C

d) How many degrees difference are there between the highest and lowest temperatures?
_____ °C

10. The number of points a football team earned during a season is shown in the table below.

Team name	Points
United	58
Rovers	74
City	64
Athletic	90
Albion	32

a) Which team earned the second least amount of points? _____

b) Which team earned the third most points? _____

/10

Test 2: Ordering and rounding whole numbers 2

1. Round these numbers to the **nearest 10**.

   a) 6478   7045   8889   5807   1555

   b) 29 837   17 995   21 001   99 507   56 219

2. Round these numbers to the **nearest 100**.

   a) 23 059   57 868   30 951   89 982   46 527

   b) 128 308   451 222   927 010   369 971   700 960

3. Round these numbers to the **nearest 1000**.

   222 481   708 564   501 901   199 489   449 738

4. Order the following numbers (smallest to largest) and then round them **to the nearest 10**. Add these numbers together to calculate an approximate answer.

   a) 1327 + 72 + 154 = _____

   Approximate answer = _____

   b) 549 + 91 + 3584 = _____

   Approximate answer = _____

   c) 2057 + 1424 + 49 = _____

   Approximate answer = _____

5. Here are the heights of six children.

   Child 1   Child 2   Child 3   Child 4   Child 5   Child 6
   124cm   131cm   120cm   141cm   135cm   149cm

   Round each child's height to the nearest 10cm.

   Child 1 _____   Child 2 _____   Child 3 _____

   Child 4 _____   Child 5 _____   Child 6 _____

6. Estimate the answers to the questions below as accurately as you can and then check your answer with a calculator.

Question	Estimate	Answer
2129 + 3454		
24 783 + 15 031		
792 + 1551		
5203 – 3487		

7. Look at these scales and estimate the weight.

_____ kg

8. The boy on the right is 123cm tall. Estimate the height of the woman standing next to him.

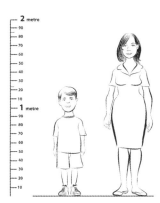

_____ cm

9. Lily can read two pages in her reading book in 246 seconds. Approximately how long will it take Lily to read 30 pages?

_____ seconds

10. Approximately, how many weeks are there in 50 years?

_____ weeks

/10

Test 3: Number patterns and sequences

1. Work out the next two numbers in this sequence.

| 3 | 6 | 12 | 24 | | |

2. Work out the next two numbers in this sequence.

| 160 | 80 | 40 | 20 | | |

3. Draw the next two shapes in this sequence.

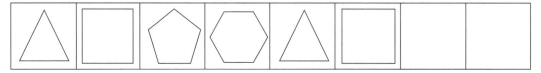

4. Work out the missing number in this sequence.

| -14 | -8 | | 4 | 10 | 16 |

5. Work out the missing numbers in this sequence.

| 13 | 5 | | -11 | -19 | |

6. The temperature in a fridge is -4°C. When the electricity is turned off, the temperature rises by 3°C every hour. What is the temperature in the fridge four hours after the electricity is turned off?

 °C

7. A liquid freezes at -16°C. A sample of the frozen liquid is heated up by 6°C every 30 minutes. What is the temperature of the liquid after two hours of heating?

_____ °C

8. Use the table to answer the questions below.

A	16	3	8	13
B	25	18	24	26
C	20	6	11	15
D	100	64	5	9

   a) Which row includes three square numbers and a factor of 20?   _____

   b) Which row includes three even numbers and one square number?   _____

   c) Which row includes two triangular numbers and one prime number?   _____

9. Complete the three gaps in this sequence.

1	4	7				19	22	25

10. A thermometer reads 27°C. If the temperature drops by 3°C every two hours, how long would it take for the temperature to reach -9°C?

   _____ hr

/10

Test 4: Factors and multiples

1. List the factors of these numbers.

   a) 32 _____

   b) 20 _____

   c) 42 _____

   d) 23 _____

2. What are the next six multiples of 5, following on from 95?

   _____ _____ _____ _____ _____ _____

3. Solve these problems involving multiples.

   a) Circle the multiples of 22.

       33   55   66   110   132

   b) Circle the multiples of 13.

       14   33   39   52   117

   c) Circle the multiples of 17.

       51   68   71   126   136

4. Circle the common multiples of 12 and 5.

      24   45   60   72   120

5. Circle the common multiples of 3 and 4.

      3   6   9   12   24

6. Solve these problems involving factors and multiples.

   a) What is the highest common factor of 12 and 20? _____

   b) What is the lowest common multiple of 6 and 8? _____

7. Pears cost eight pence each and apples cost seven pence each. If Jane spends 60 pence, how many apples and pears can she buy without having any change left over?

_____

8. Jake and Kadir are texting on their phones. Jake sends a text to Kadir every 30 seconds, Kadir sends a text every 45 seconds. If they both send their first text at the same time, how many texts does Jake send before both the boys send a text at the same time again (not counting the first text sent)?

_____

9. School buses arrive from Eastfield every six minutes and Westfield every nine minutes. If the buses both arrive at 08:15, when will they both arrive together again?

_____

10. Add the factors of 32 to the factors of 11 and subtract the first two multiples of nine. What is the final number?

_____

/10

Test 5: Adding whole numbers

1. Calculate the answer to the following additions.

   a) Thirteen add fifty-eight _____

   b) Seventy-five add thirty-four _____

   c) Forty-six add ninety-seven _____

2. Add these numbers.

   a) 128 + 308 _____

   b) 437 + 292 _____

   c) 830 + 405 _____

3. Now work these out.

a)	45	b)	83	c)	72
	+61		+39		+29
	____		____		____

4. Calculate the additions below.

a)	138	b)	528	c)	631
	+457		+604		+729
	____		____		____

5. Add together 583, 692, 571, 904 and 300.

   _____

6. A census is taken to find the population of the city and some towns and hamlets in the Blackburn area. The results are as follows:

   999   72 633   105 085   19   4506

   What is the total population? _____

7. Add the first three triangular numbers to the first three square numbers.

   _____

8. How many metres of tape are needed to mark out all of the lines on this netball court?

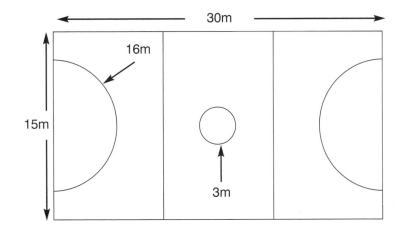

_____ m

9. Work out the following addition calculations.

a) 120 + (-22) =   _____

b) (-120) + (-22) =   _____

c) 12 + (-3) + (-3) + (-3) + (-3) =   _____

10. Write in the missing digits to complete the calculation correctly.

8		9	+		6	4	=	9	9	3

/10

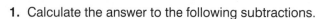

Test 6: Subtracting whole numbers

1. Calculate the answer to the following subtractions.

   a) Seventy-three subtract twenty-seven   _____

   b) Ninety-four subtract thirty-six   _____

   c) Fifty-one subtract eighteen   _____

2. Subtract these numbers.

   a) 571 – 358   _____

   b) 907 – 668   _____

   c) 325 – 179   _____

3. Calculate the subtractions below.

   a)   82   **b)**   53   **c)**   61
          −34   −37   −19
          ____   ____   ____

4. Find the answers to these subtractions.

   a)   742   **b)**   259   **c)**   1058
          −178   − 83   − 591
          _____   ____   _____

5. Take away 265 096 from 1 062 884.

   _____

6. Work out the following subtraction calculations.

   a) 368 – (-26) =   _____

   b) -368 – (-26) =   _____

   c) -15 – (-15) – (-30) = _____

7. The temperature in Abu Dhabi is 45°C, in Santiago it is -7°C and in Krakow it is -22°C.

   a) What is the difference between the highest and lowest temperatures? _____ °C

   b) If all the temperatures rose by 8°C, what would be the new temperature in each city?

   _____ °C   _____ °C   _____ °C

   c) If all the temperatures dropped by 9°C, what would be the new temperature in each city?

   _____ °C   _____ °C   _____ °C

8. A baker has 6kg of flour. He needs 225g of flour for one cake. If he makes 12 cakes, how much flour will be left?

   _____ kg

9. A full storage tank holds 520 litres of water. The tank is drained by opening the tap. 40 litres of water is drained out through the tap every minute. How many minutes will it take until the tank holds only 200 litres?

   _____ min

10. Write in the missing digits.

| 9 | 4 | | − | 3 | 9 | 8 | = | | 4 | 6 |

/10

Test 7: Multiplying whole numbers

1. Find the product of the following numbers.

   a) 30 and 6 _____

   b) 300 and 6 _____

   c) 3000 and 60 _____

2. Circle the number which, when multiplied by 5, gives a multiple of 18.

   5   25   90   120   505

3. Multiply 2^2 by 5^2 _____

4. Calculate the answers to these multiplications.

   a) $12 \times 7 =$ _____   **b)** $20 \times 3 =$ _____

   c) $6 \times 15 =$ _____   **d)** $9 \times 18 =$ _____

5. Calculate 24×37.

   _____

6. Calculate 146×17.

   _____

7. 87 people have come to watch a film at the cinema. They each pay £4 each to get in. How much money does the cinema take?

   £_____

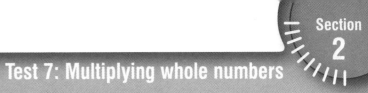
8. A music concert has 54 rows of seats. There are 28 seats in each row. How many people can be seated during the concert?

_____ people

9. A box of marbles has 35 marbles in it. There are 24 boxes in the shop. How many marbles does the shop have altogether?

_____ marbles

10. Teachers at a playgroup are buying balloons for their end-of-term party. Each pack contains six balloons. The teachers bought 15 packs of large balloons and 10 packs of small balloons. How many balloons did they have altogether?

_____ balloons

/10

1. Write down the quotient of these numbers.

   a) 81 and 9 _____   **b)** 56 and 7 _____   **c)** 108 and 9 _____

2. Divide 12^2 by 2^3.

   _____

3. What is the square root of 169?

   _____

4. Calculate the answers to these division problems.

   a) $84 \div 4 =$ _____   **b)** $72 \div 9 =$ _____

   c) $120 \div 5 =$ _____   **d)** $91 \div 7 =$ _____

5. Calculate $245 \div 7$.

   _____

6. Calculate $666 \div 9$.

   _____

7. Olivia has 97 sweets in a jar. She shares the sweets equally between herself and three of her friends. How many sweets does each child have? How many are left over?

   _____ sweets each

   _____ left over

8. There are 472 children at a football tournament. Teams are made up of eight players. How many teams are there altogether?

_____ teams

9. Fancy Mugs have a busy day sending out their orders. It takes 30cm of paper to wrap up each mug, and they have ten 2-metre rolls of paper. How many mugs can Fancy Mugs send out today before they use up all their paper?

_____ mugs

10. Kate has £200 to spend on her birthday party. Party bags cost £5 each and food costs £2 for each person. How many children can she invite so that Kate and her friends can all have food and a party bag?

_____ friends

/10

1. Add brackets to make these calculations correct.

   a) 6 × 5 + 4 × 5 = 170   _____

   b) 6 × 5 + 4 × 5 = 50   _____

2. Jake has 750ml of lemonade left after pouring glasses for five friends from his 2-litre jug. Then 13 more friends turn up. How many more 2-litre bottles does Jake have to buy so that everybody can have a glass?

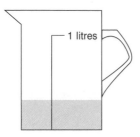
1 litres

_____ bottles

3. Archie and Lizzie are throwing dice. The chart shows how many times they throw each number.

Number on dice	6	5	4	3	2	1
Archie	3	4	4	2	1	3
Lizzie	4	3	7	1	1	1

   a) If the results of all the throws are added together, who got the highest total?

   _____

   b) What was the highest total?   _____

4. A forklift driver is checking through the packages that are scheduled to move to the loading bay that day. The maximum load for her truck is one tonne. How many journeys must she make to transfer all the packages?

Package weight (kg)	Number of packages
490	2
50	6
150	2
550	2
10	10

_____ journeys

Test 9: Solving problems involving the four operations

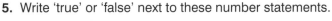

5. Write 'true' or 'false' next to these number statements.

    a) $(130 \times 3) \times (14 \times 0) = 5460$ _____

    b) $\frac{(81\,000)}{9} = 900$ _____

    c) $29 \times 31 = 899$ _____

6. Complete the table below.

+	199	2999	9999
9			
99			
999			

7. 15 children go to a pizzeria. All the children choose from the specials board: two courses cost £7, three courses cost £8.

    The total bill comes to £111. How many children had three courses?

    _____ children

8. A gymnastics club has 70 members. The table below shows some information collected at their registration.

	Girls	Boys	Total
Northtown		19	41
Southtown			
Total	31	39	

    How many members of the club come from Southtown? _____

9. $555 \times 666 = 369\,630$

    ... so what does 556×666 equal? Underline the correct answer.

    370 296   307 269   470 296   407 206   372 960

10. Mrs Visana has 429 pencils. She packs them into boxes of 70.

    a) How many boxes does she fill? _____ boxes

    b) How many pencils are left over? _____ pencils

/10

1. Work out the value of q in the following equation.

   $215 - q = 148$ _____

2. What is the value of z in the equation below?

   $z + 92 = 308$ _____

3. $s + t + w = 112$; if $s = 32$ and $t = w$, what is the value of w?

   _____

4. If $y = 6$, write 'true' or 'false' next to the following statements.

   a) $9y + 7y = 98$ _____

   b) $3y \times 8 = 144$ _____

   c) $\dfrac{36y}{36} = 6$ _____

5. There is a ratio of one adult to three children going into the cinema to watch a film. If x is the number of children and y is the number of adults, write a formula, in terms of y only, for the number of people at a single viewing.

   _____

6. Look at the following equation.

   $z + 31 = 58$

   What is the value of z?

   $z =$ _____

7. Read the statements below and then answer the question.

Jenny is x years old.

Suri is three years older than Jenny.

Louise is twice as old as Suri.

Work out an expression for Louise's age. _____

8. Phoebe's older brother has come up with a scheme for making money. He has offered to help Phoebe with her homework at a rate of 50 pence for the first hour and 20 pence per additional hour. Which of these expressions gives the cost in pence for homework lasting x hours?

A $50 + 20(x - 1)$ **B** $50x + 20$ **C** $20x + 50$ **D** $50 + x + 20$

_____

9. $a = 9, b = 2a, c = b - a$

What is the value of c if a is doubled? $c = $ _____

10. $66z = 11y$. If $z = 7$:

What is the value of y? $y = $ _____

/10

Test 11: Fractions and fraction calculations

1. Put the following fractions in the correct place in the sorting diagram below:

$$\frac{1}{2} \qquad \frac{11}{8} \qquad \frac{8}{10} \qquad 6\frac{1}{3} \qquad \frac{6}{4} \qquad 3\frac{7}{12}$$

Proper fraction	Improper fraction	Mixed number fraction

2. Look at the shapes below. What fraction of each shape is shaded, in simplest terms?

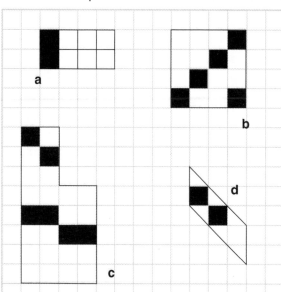

a = _____

b = _____

c = _____

d = _____

3. Put the following fractions in the correct order from smallest to largest.

$$\frac{2}{5} \qquad \frac{6}{4} \qquad \frac{1}{3} \qquad \frac{8}{10} \qquad \frac{7}{15} \qquad \frac{1}{2}$$

_____   _____   _____   _____   _____   _____

4. Simplify the following fractions.

a) $\frac{16}{24}$ _____

b) $\frac{24}{72}$ _____

c) $\frac{21}{28}$ _____

d) $\frac{42}{56}$ _____

e) $\frac{9}{18}$ _____

f) $\frac{300}{75}$ _____

5. Add $\frac{1}{2} + \frac{1}{3} + \frac{1}{4}$, then write your answer as a mixed number.

_____

6. What is $\frac{3}{4}$ of 4.4 litres?

_____ litres

7. Aaron's family is sharing out the loose change in the piggy bank. He receives $\frac{2}{7}$ of the money. The amount he gets is £3.80.

How much money was in the piggy bank before Aaron took his share?

£ _____

8. There are 92 chocolates in a tin. Of these $\frac{1}{4}$ have soft centres, the rest have hard centres.

How many of the chocolates have hard centres? _____

9. A fully loaded car weighs 1430kg. The passengers weigh $\frac{2}{5}$ of the total weight.

How much does the car weigh without the passengers inside? _____ kg

10. Look at the jug of water below.

2 litres

The jug is $\frac{4}{5}$ full. How much water is in the jug?

_____ ml

/10

Test 12: Decimals

1. Put a circle around the largest decimal below.

8.02   8.002   8.2   8.022   8.020

2. Write the value of the digit in bold in each number in words.

a) 14.0**5**   _____   **b)** 14.**5**   _____

c) 14.00**5**   _____

3. Double the following decimals.

a) 0.3   _____   **b)** 1.4   _____

c) 3.82   _____   **d)** 0.09   _____

4. Match the calculations in the first column to the calculations in the second column which have identical answers.

3.6 × 0.8		66 + 22.9
2.88 × 0		0.99 + 0.392
6.91 × 0.2		1.44 × 2
89.89 – 0.99		2.78 (3.66 × 0)

5. Work out the answers to these calculations.

a) 3.8 – 2.2 =   _____

b) 4.9 + 6.3 =   _____

c) 18.09 – 4.2 =   _____

d) 23.6 + 14.23 =   _____

6. Clive has a weekly shopping list. This week he decides to get two weeks' worth of shopping in one go. Write the new amounts Clive must get.

	Old amount	New amount
Carrots	1200g	kg
Potatoes	2.5kg	kg
Tomatoes	0.45kg	kg
Onions	3	
Peas	300g	kg

7. Class 3 did a sponsored walk. They split into six groups and the money they raised was as follows:

Group 1 = £13.28   Group 2 = £10.50   Group 3 = 1571p

Group 4 = £8   Group 5 = 1108p   Group 6 = £12.99

How much money did Class 3 raise altogether? £ _____

8. Here are the weights of some children. Work out how much they weigh altogether.

25.4kg   28.72kg   21.8kg   30.02kg   33.19kg   24.5kg

_____ kg

9. A jug can hold 2200ml of water. It takes 100 jugs of water to fill a tank. How much water can the tank hold if it is full?

_____ litres

10. Tallulah measures her stride. It is 85cm. If Tallulah takes 200 strides, how many metres has she travelled?

_____ m

/10

Test 13: Finding equivalents

1. Complete the table below.

Original	35%	0.61	$\frac{17}{25}$	53%	$\frac{13}{20}$
Decimal	0.35				
Difference from 0.8	0.45				

2. What is the difference between the largest decimal and smallest decimal in the middle row of the table above?

_____

3. Find the percentage equivalents to these fractions.

a) $\frac{1}{8}$ _____%

b) $\frac{3}{5}$ _____%

c) $\frac{1}{20}$ _____%

d) $\frac{1}{25}$ _____%

4. Find the decimal equivalents to these fractions.

a) $\frac{13}{100}$ _____

b) $\frac{7}{25}$ _____

c) $\frac{4}{5}$ _____

d) $\frac{1}{3}$ _____

5. Circle the smallest of these quantities.

A 2.3%   **B** 0.23   **C** $\frac{2}{3}$ **D** $\frac{1}{23}$ **E** 0.0023

6. Which of these options is closest to $\frac{1}{2}$?

A 52%   **B** 0.501   **C** $\frac{13}{25}$ **D** 0.5001   **E** $\frac{17}{50}$

a) Circle the correct letter.

b) Which two answer options have the same value?   _____

200 children had pizza on a school trip and they all had additional toppings. The percentages of children who chose each topping are shown on the chart.

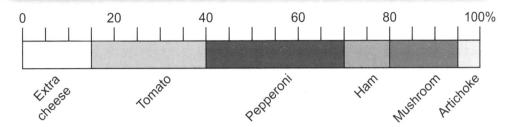

7. Use the chart to work out...

a) The percentage of children who had extra cheese. _____%

b) The number of children who had pepperoni. _____

c) The percentage of children who had tomato. _____%

8. If half the children who chose pepperoni changed their minds and had artichoke instead, what fraction, expressed as a decimal, would have had artichoke?

_____

9. What percentage of this shape is shaded?

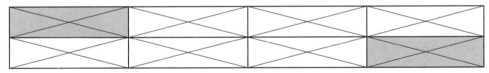

_____ %

10. Circle the statements that are correct.

A $9.6 > 96\%$ **B** $9.6 = \dfrac{960}{100}$ **C** $9.6 > 96$ **D** $9\dfrac{1}{6} < 9\dfrac{1}{12}$ **E** $0.96 > 96\%$

/10

1. Complete the chart.

£	1%	10%	21%	79%
436				
1671				
2316				

2. Which of these amounts in the larger? Underline your answer.

a) 50% of 110 or 20% of 300?   **b)** 90% of 900 or 10% of 9000?

c) 15% of 800 or 25% of 320?   **d)** 20% of 640 or 50% of 260?

e) 20% of 400 or 80% of 60?   **f)** 99% of 100 or 100% of 98?

3. Jessica has 60 paperbacks, 18 of which are holiday romances. What percentage of Jessica's total collection are her holiday romance books?

_____%

4. What percentages of the grids below are shaded?

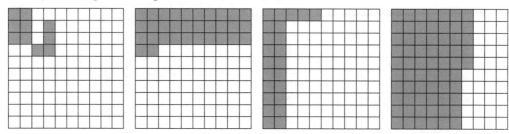

a _____%   b _____%   c _____%   d _____%

5. Calculate 50% of the following amounts.

a) 42kg   _____ kg

b) 64 litres   _____ litres

c) 3km   _____ km

d) £70   £ _____

Maths 10-Minute Tests Answers

Test 1
1. 10 835
2. **a)** two hundred **b)** two thousand **c)** twenty thousand
3. **a)** 1825, 1852, 2185, 2851, 3518
   b) 6001, 6099, 6430, 6515, 7000
4. **a)** 11 111, 10 380, 10 307, 10 019, 9984
   b) 49 984, 40 621, 40 440, 40 019, 5987
5. **a)** 190, 19, 0, -19, -20
   b) 40 621, 40 440, 40 019, -5987, -49 984
6. -120
7. 8970
8. **a)** Billy **b)** Eric **c)** Jon
9. **a)** C, A, B, D, E **b)** 6°C **c)** 1°C **d)** 22°C
10. **a)** United **b)** City

Test 2
1. **a)** 6480, 7050, 8890, 5810, 1560
   b) 29 840, 18 000, 21 000, 99 510, 56 220
2. **a)** 23 100, 57 900, 31 000, 90 000, 46 500
   b) 128 300, 451 200, 927 000, 370 000, 701 000
3. 222 000, 709 000, 502 000, 199 000, 450 000
4. **a)** 72, 154, 1327; 70, 150, 1330; 1550
   b) 91, 549, 3584; 90, 550, 3580; 4220
   c) 49, 1424, 2057; 50, 1420, 2060; 3530
5. Child 1 = 120cm, Child 2 = 130cm, Child 3 = 120cm
   Child 4 = 140cm, Child 5 = 140cm, Child 6 = 150cm
6.

Question	Estimate	Answer
2129 + 3454	**5580 or 5600**	5583
24 783 + 15 031	**39 810 or 39 800**	39 814
792 + 1551	**2340 or 2350**	2343
5203 – 3487	**1720 or 1700**	1716

7. Answers between 13kg and 14kg
8. Answers between 180cm and 190cm
9. Answers around 3750 seconds
10. Answers between 2500 weeks and 2600 weeks

Test 3
1.

3	6	12	24	**48**	**96**

2.

160	80	40	20	**10**	5

3.

4.

-14	-8	**-2**	4	10	16

5.

13	5	**-3**	-11	-19	**-27**

6. 8°C
7. 8°C
8. **a)** D **b)** B **c)** C
9.

1	4	7	**10**	**13**	**16**	19	22	25

10. 24hr

Test 4
1. **a)** 1, 2, 4, 8, 16, 32 **b)** 1, 2, 4, 5, 10, 20 **c)** 1, 2, 3, 6, 7, 14, 21, 42
   d) 1, 23

2. 100, 105, 110, 115, 120, 125
3. **a)** 66, 110, 132 **b)** 39, 52, 117 **c)** 51, 68, 136
4. 60, 120
5. 12, 24
6. **a)** 4 **b)** 24
7. 4 pears and 4 apples
8. 3 texts
9. 08:33 or 8:33
10. 48
    factors of 32: 1, 2, 4, 8, 16, 32
    factors of 11: 1, 11
    first two multiples of 9: 9, 18
    63 + 12 − 27 = 48

Test 5
1. **a)** 71 **b)** 109 **c)** 143
2. **a)** 436 **b)** 729 **c)** 1235
3. **a)** 106 **b)** 122 **c)** 101
4. **a)** 595 **b)** 1132 **c)** 1360
5. 3050
6. 183242
7. 1 + 3 + 6 + 1 + 4 + 9 = 24
8. 155m
9. **a)** 98 **b)** -142 **c)** 0
10. 829 + 164 = 993

Test 6
1. **a)** 46 **b)** 58 **c)** 33
2. **a)** 213 **b)** 239 **c)** 146
3. **a)** 48 **b)** 16 **c)** 42
4. **a)** 564 **b)** 176 **c)** 467
5. 797 788
6. **a)** 394 **b)** -342 **c)** 30
7. **a)** 67°C **b)** 53°C, 1°C, -14°C **c)** 36°C, -16°C, -31°C
8. 3.3kg
9. 8min
10. 944 – 398 = 546

Test 7
1. **a)** 180 **b)** 1800 **c)** 180 000
2. 90
3. 100
4. **a)** 84 **b)** 60 **c)** 90 **d)** 162
5. 888
6. 2482
7. £348
8. 1512 people
9. 840 marbles
10. 150 balloons

Test 8
1. **a)** 9 **b)** 8 **c)** 12
2. 18
3. 13
4. **a)** 21 **b)** 8 **c)** 24 **d)** 13
5. 35
6. 74
7. 24 sweets each
   1 sweet left over
8. 59 teams
9. 66 mugs
10. 27 friends (this number does not include Kate)

Test 9
1. **a)** (6 × 5 + 4) × 5 = 170
   b) (6 × 5) + (4 × 5) = 50
2. 2 bottles
3. **a)** Lizzie **b)** 73
4. 3 journeys
5. **a)** false **b)** false **c)** true
6.

+	199	2999	9999
9	208	3008	10 008
99	298	3098	10 098
999	1198	3998	10 998

7. 6 children
8. 29 members
9. 370 296
10. **a)** 6 boxes **b)** 9 pencils

1

Test 10
1. 67
2. 216
3. 40
4. a) false b) true c) true
5. $4y$
6. 27
7. $2(x + 3)$
8. A
9. 18
10. 42

Test 11
1.

Proper fraction	Improper fraction	Mixed number fraction
$\frac{1}{2}$	$\frac{11}{8}$	$6\frac{1}{3}$
$\frac{8}{10}$	$\frac{6}{4}$	$3\frac{7}{12}$

2. $a=\frac{1}{4}$ $b=\frac{5}{16}$ $c=\frac{3}{13}$ $d=\frac{1}{3}$
3. $\frac{1}{3}, \frac{2}{5}, \frac{7}{15}, \frac{1}{2}, \frac{8}{10}, \frac{6}{4}$
4. a) $\frac{2}{3}$ b) $\frac{1}{3}$ c) $\frac{3}{4}$ d)) $\frac{3}{4}$ e) $\frac{1}{2}$ f) 4
5. $1\frac{1}{12}$
6. 3.3 litres
7. £13.30
8. 69
9. 858kg
10. 1600ml

Test 12
1. 8.2
2. a) five hundredths
   b) five tenths
   c) five thousandths
3. a) 0.6 b) 2.8 c) 7.64 d) 0.18
4.

3.6 × 0.8	66 + 22.9
2.88 × 0	0.99 + 0.392
6.91 × 0.2	1.44 × 2
89.89 − 0.99	2.78 (3.66 × 0)

5. a) 1.6 b) 11.2 c) 13.89 d) 37.83
6.

	Old amount	New amount
Carrots	1200g	**2.4kg**
Potatoes	2.5kg	**5kg**
Tomatoes	0.45kg	**0.9kg**
Onions	3	**6**
Peas	300g	**0.6kg**

7. £71.56
8. 163.63kg
9. 220 litres
10. 170m

Test 13
1.

Original	35%	0.61	$\frac{13}{20}$	53%	$\frac{13}{20}$
Decimal	0.35	**0.61**	**0.68**	**0.53**	**0.65**
Difference from 0.8	0.45	**0.19**	**0.12**	**0.27**	**0.15**

2. 0.33
3. a) 12.5% b) 60% c) 5% d) 4%
4. a) 0.13 b) 0.28 c) 0.8 d) 0.333
5. E
6. a) D b) A and C
7. a) 15% b) 60 children c) 25%
8. 0.2
9. 25%
10. A, B

Test 14
1.

£	1%	10%	21%	79%
436	4.36	43.60	91.56	344.44
1671	16.71	167.10	350.91	1320.09
2316	23.16	231.60	486.36	1829.64

2. a) 20% of 300 b) 10% of 9000
   c) 15% of 800 d) 50% of 260
   e) 20% of 400 f) 99% of 100
3. 30%
4. a) 10% b) 32% c) 23% d) 65%
5. a) 21kg b) 32 litres c) 1.5km d) £35
6. a) £36 b) 60m c) £1.20 d) 180kg
7. £2
8. £321
9. 82.8kg
10. 1000km

Test 15
1. $\frac{3}{8}$
2. $\frac{5}{8}$
3. 6:4 or 3:2
4. 24
5. 24:16 or 12:8 or 6:4 or 3:2
6. 10:6 or 5:3
7. $\frac{3}{8}$
8. boys = 9, girls = 9
9. 6 adults
10. 7:5

Test 16
1. £2000
2. £900
3.

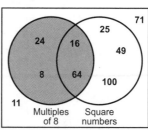

4. Any square number that is a multiple of 8, not shown in the answer options for question 3, e.g. 144, 256, 6400
5. 294km
6. 99km
7. 465km
8. Quadtower to Byton or vice versa
9.

Insects	Tally	Frequency
Ants	IIII IIII IIII IIII IIII	25
Woodlice	IIII IIII IIII	14
Earwigs	IIII IIII	9
Ladybirds	IIII IIII IIII IIII	19
Hover flies	IIII IIII IIII IIII I	21

10. 88 insects

Test 17
1. 26 bars (accept 24 to 28)
2. 28 bars (accept 26 to 30)
3. £6
4. £41 (accept 40 to 42)
5. 45 children (accept 42 to 48)
6. 10 children (accept 7 to 13)
7. 13 children (accept 10 to 15)
8. 20:00 or 8pm
9. 26°C (accept 25°C to 27°C)
10. 13:00 or 1pm (accept 12:30 to 13:30)

Test 18
1. 12
2. Jake
3. 8.4
4. 21
5. 22
6. Mode 15, Mean 13, Median 13, Range 12
7. Grey
8. £11.80
9. Radcliffe
10. Mode 2, Median 3, Range 4

Test 19
1. Black
2. White and grey
3. 2
4. 10%
5. Grey
6. B
7. B
8. C
9. C and D
10. B and D

Test 20
1. **a)** isosceles **b)** 5 **c)** no **d)** 7 **e)** 4
2. 15cm
3.

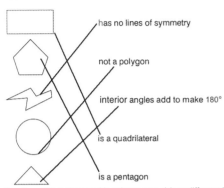

- has no lines of symmetry
- not a polygon
- interior angles add to make 180°
- is a quadrilateral
- is a pentagon

4. Any four-sided shape with at least one side a different length
5. **a)** 1 **b)** trapezium
6.

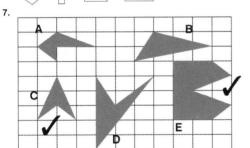

7.

8. 6
9. A and D
10. 105°

Test 21
1. **a)** 6 **b)** 3 **c)** 1
2. **a)** 12 **b)** 1 **c)** 8
3. **a)** 0 **b)** 8 **c)** 4
4. B and C
5. Tetrahedron/triangular-based pyramid
6. **a)** 4 **b)** 5 **c)** 9
7. 16 straws
8. **a)** hexagonal-based pyramid
   b) cylinder
   c) triangular prism
9. Any two of: sphere, cylinder, ovoid, hemisphere
10. Square-based pyramid

Test 22
1.

- reflex angle
- acute angle
- right angle
- obtuse angle

2. Answers between: $x = 20°$ to $30°$ and $y = 65°$ to $75°$
3. Answers between: $a = 130°$ to $140°$ and $b = 95°$ to $105°$
4. 110°
5. 70°
6. 130° (126° to 134° is acceptable)

7. 40° (36° to 44° is acceptable)
8. Answers ± 3°: $a = 50°$, $b = 100°$, $c = 30°$
9. 235° (231° to 239° is acceptable)
10. Answers ± 4°: $s = 140°$, $t = 320°$

Test 23
1. 40cm
2. 11cm²
3. 6.4cm
4. 5512m²
5.

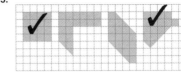

6. 119cm²
7. 314cm²
8. 150m³
9. 100cm²
10. 343cm³

Test 24
1. A = (1, 4) B = (3, 6) C = (3, 0) D = (5, 1)
2. A = (1, 0) B = (2, 6) C = (7, 8) D = (9, 4)
3.

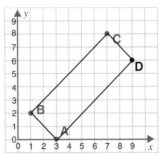

4. P = (0.2, 0.6) Q = (0.6, 0.9) R = (0.7, 0.5) S = (0.5, 0.1)
5. B = (0, 13) C = (2, 1) D = (3, 11) E = (10, 6)
6.

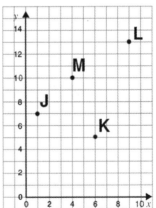

7. **a)** Park (17, 12) **b)** Market (3, 14) **c)** Pool (16, 1)
8. M = (-1, 1) N = (1, 4) O = (-3, -2) P = (2, -5)
9.

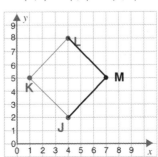

10.

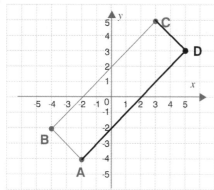

Test 25

1.

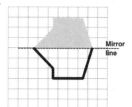

2.

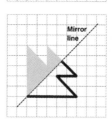

3. H and B

4. C

5.

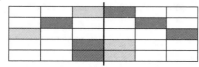

6.

7.

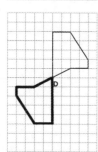

8.

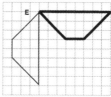

9.

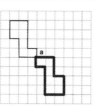

10.

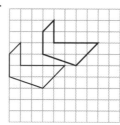

Test 26

1. **a)** 300cm **b)** 4.5cm **c)** 3500m
2. **a)** 3.5kg **b)** 0.75 tonnes **c)** 4060g
3. **a)** 35ml **b)** 3.45 litres **c)** 9052ml
4. **a)** 2.2 pounds **b)** accept 39 or 40 inches **c)** 2 gallons
5. 2.2 litres
6. **a)** 7.6cm or 76mm **b)** 4.2cm or 42mm **c)** 5.5cm or 55mm
7. 1kg
8. 15 000ml
9. 14km
10. **a)** 15°C **b)** 17°C **c)** -13°C

Test 27

1. $\frac{1}{6}$ 2. 2700 seconds
3. 255min   4. 1440min
5. **a)** 12th September 2012
   b) 27th August
6. **a)** 55min
   b) 20:20
7. Monday
8. 80 minutes or 1 hour and 20 minutes
9. 29min 45 seconds
10. 140min

Test 28

1. B   2. fd1, R, fd3, L, fd7
3. fd1, L, fd2   4. 10:22 (10 tables, 22 chairs)
5. 40 cards

Test 29

1. 4000   2. 32 and 64
3. 40   4. 59
5. 987   6. 5
7. 800   8. 90km
9. 30 sweets   10. 51
11. 13   12. $\frac{2}{5}$
13. £120   14. $\frac{2}{3}$
15. 4   16. 180°
17. 5   18. 1200m²
19. 77.5   20. 00:23

6. Calculate 30% of the following amounts.

 a) £120   £ _____

 b) 200m   _____ m

 c) £4.00   £ _____

 d) 600kg   _____ kg

7. There is a sale in a local games shop. The sign says 25% off. Iva buys a game that originally cost £24. How much change does Iva get from £20?

 £ _____

8. Damon puts £300 in a bank account. The money earns 7% interest per year. How much money does Damon have in the account after 1 year's interest is added?

 £ _____

9. A man who weighs 92kg decides to go on a diet. He loses 10% of his weight. What is his new weight?

 _____ kg

10. A road is 800km long. The length is increased by 25%. How long is the road now?

 _____ km

/10

Test 15: Ratio and proportion

1. What proportion of this square is shaded? Give your answer as a fraction, in simplest terms.

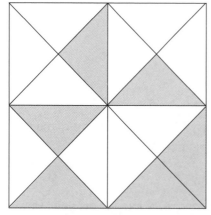

2. What proportion of this regular octagon is shaded? Give your answer as a fraction.

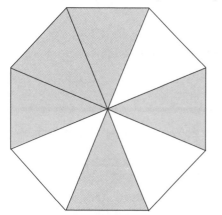

3. In a group of 10 children, four are boys and six are girls.

   What is the ratio of girls to boys?

   _____

4. There is a mixture of 14 red and yellow flowers in a bunch. The ratio of yellow to red is 6:1.

   What is the total number of yellow flowers in two bunches?

   _____

5. In a box of 40 marbles, there are 24 black marbles and 16 white marbles.

   What is the ratio of black to white marbles?

   _____

Liam and Lucy's mum is putting in a new bathroom. The box of tiles she has bought contains a mixture of grey and white tiles.

6. What is the ratio of grey tiles to white tiles?

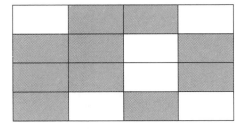

_____

7. What proportion of the tiles is white?

Give your answer as a fraction in its simplest form.

$$\frac{\boxed{}}{\boxed{}}$$

8. In a group of 18 children, the ratio of boys to girls is 1:1.

How many boys and girls are there in the group?

boys _____

girls _____

9. Kelly has a birthday party. The ratio of children to adults is 4:1.

There are 24 children at the party. How many adults are there?

_____ adults

10. Look at the cups of coffee on the tray.

What is the ratio of black cups to white cups?

_____

/10

The bar chart below shows the amount of money a shop took in one week.

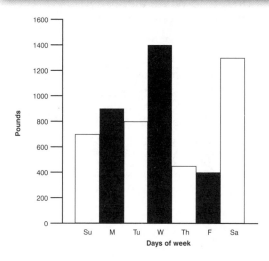

1. How much money did the shop take at the weekend?

£ _____

2. How much money did the shop take on Monday?

£ _____

Molly has drawn a Venn diagram to help her to work out some maths problems.

3. Write these numbers on the diagram to help arrange her data.

8   11   16   24   25   49   64   71   100

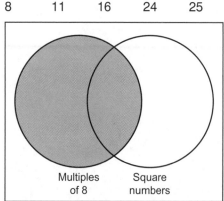

4. Find another square number that she could put into the space where the circles overlap.

_____

The distance chart below shows the distance in kilometres between seven towns.

Octford						
564	Hepton					
464	143	Hexmouth				
321	243	214	Pentdon			
294	114	161	36	Quadtower		
394	313	71	114	16	Tryton	
146	342	96	64	13	99	Bytown

5. How far is it from Octford to Quadtower?

_____ km

6. How far is it from Tryton to Bytown?

_____ km

7. If you travelled from Hexmouth to Tryton and then onwards from Tryton to Octford, how far would you have gone?

_____ km

8. What is the shortest single journey shown on the chart?

_____ to _____

The tally chart shows the number of insects Daryl collected in his garden during one day.

Insects	Tally	Frequency
Ants	⊬⊬⊬ ⊬⊬⊬ ⊬⊬⊬ ⊬⊬⊬ ⊬⊬⊬	
Woodlice		14
Earwigs	⊬⊬⊬ ||||	9
Ladybirds	⊬⊬⊬ ⊬⊬⊬ ⊬⊬⊬ ||||	
Hover flies	⊬⊬⊬ ⊬⊬⊬ ⊬⊬⊬ ⊬⊬⊬ |	21

9. Complete the tally chart.

10. What was the total number of insects Daryl collected?

_____ insects

/10

The number of chocolate bars sold at a school tuck shop during one week is shown on the pictogram.

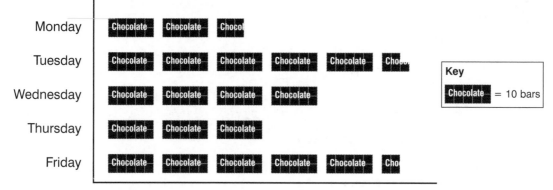

Key	
Chocolate	= 10 bars

1. How many chocolate bars were sold on Monday?

_____ bars

2. How many more chocolate bars were sold on Friday than Monday?

_____ bars

The bar chart shows the pocket money six children received in one week.

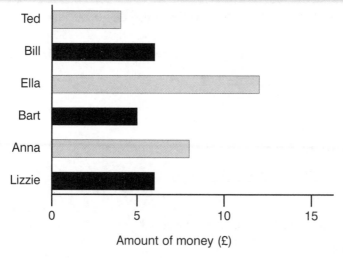

Amount of money (£)

3. How much pocket money did Bill get?

£ _____

4. How much money did the children receive altogether?

£ _____

The pie chart below shows the sort of pets 100 children have.

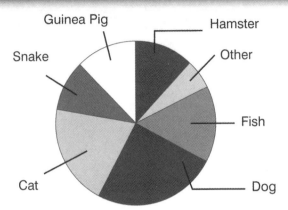

5. Approximately, how many children have a dog or a cat? _____

6. Estimate the number of children who have a pet snake. _____

7. Estimate how many more children have a dog than a hamster. _____

The line graph represents the temperature recorded in a conservatory. The readings were taken at two-hour intervals.

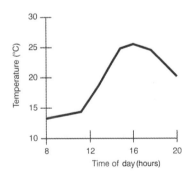

8. At what time was the last temperature reading taken?

_____

9. What was the approximate temperature at 4pm?

_____°C

10. When did the temperature first hit 20°C?

_____

/10

1. Write down the mode in this list of ten numbers.

| 12 | 14 | 9 | 14 | 12 | 12 | 9 | 15 | 18 | 4 |

_____

2. Write down the modal name out of this group.

Haresh	Jake
Bart	Mick
Will	Jake
Jack	Jack
Jake	Bart
Haresh	Callum

_____

3. Calculate the mean in this list of ten numbers.

| 8 | 7 | 7 | 9 | 4 | 12 | 10 | 7 | 11 | 9 |

_____

4. Circle the median number in this list.

| 11 | 12 | 18 | 21 | 25 | 26 | 34 |

5. Find the median number in these 11 numbers.

| 24 | 18 | 19 | 28 | 30 | 9 | 43 | 57 | 16 | 22 | 1 |

_____

6. Find the mode, mean, median and range of this set of numbers.

| 15 | 12 | 8 | 15 | 15 | 8 | 10 | 10 | 17 | 13 | 20 |

Mode	
Mean	
Median	
Range	

Test 18: Finding the mode, median, mean and range

7. Look at the box of tiles below.

What is the modal colour of the tiles?

_____

8. A group of children do a sponsored walk. Here is the amount of money each child raised.

Name	Amount (£)
Jess	10.20
Kate	12.90
Paul	8.50
Ganga	14.00
Raul	13.40

What is the mean amount of money raised per child?

£ _____

9. Nine athletes ran in a 100m race. Here are their finishing times:

Lane	Name	Time (seconds)
1	Radcliffe	10.00
2	Begum	9.82
3	Doyle	10.07
4	Brown	10.30
5	Jones	9.84
6	MacBeath	10.22
7	Day	9.90
8	Edwards	10.12
9	Dubashi	9.91

Which athlete ran the median time?

_____

10. The dance class all need new ballet shoes. The table shows the sizes and quantities that are needed.

Shoe sizes	1	2	3	4	5
Frequency	3	7	4	5	4

Mode	
Median	
Range	

Now complete the table on the right.

/10

1. What colour ball is the most likely to be drawn out of the bag below?

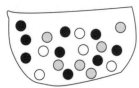

_____

2. Which colour balls are equally likely to be drawn from the bag below?

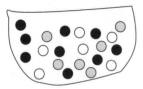

_____ and _____

3. Look at the spinner below. Which number is most likely to come up?

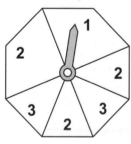

_____

4. Look at the spinner below. What is the probability of the spinner landing on the white section, expressed as a percentage?

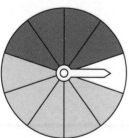

_____%

5. Look at the spinner below. Which colour is least likely to come up?

_____

6. Naseef has a bag of marbles. There are seven red marbles, four green marbles, six white marbles and three black marbles. Naseef picks a marble from the bag at random. Underline the statement below which is true.

   A There is an even chance of picking a red marble.

   B Naseef is twice as likely to pick a white marble than a black marble.

   C Naseef is certain to pick a red or white marble.

   D He has no chance of picking a black marble.

7. Megan rolls two six-sided dice, the faces of each being numbered 1 to 6. She then adds the two numbers together. Underline the statement below which is true.

   A Megan is certain to roll two sixes.

   B She is most likely to get a total of seven.

   C Megan will get a total that is an even number.

   D She will not get a total of seven.

8. Which spinner below has the most chance of coming up with a 1?

   A   B   C   D   _____

9. Tick the statements below which are correct.

   A It is certain to rain today.

   B It is likely to go dark tonight.

   C Tomorrow is the day after today.

   D I am certain to be older tomorrow.

10. Tick the statements below which are incorrect.

   A It is certain to go dark tonight.

   B Tomorrow it is certain to snow.

   C It is unlikely I will ever be a king or queen.

   D The sun is likely to set today.

/10

Test 20: 2-D shapes

1. Fill in the gaps to make the following sentences correct.

   a) _____ triangles have one line of symmetry and two equal sides.

   b) A regular pentagon has _____ lines of symmetry.

   c) A scalene triangle has _____ equal sides.

   d) A regular heptagon has _____ equal angles.

   e) A rhombus has _____ equal sides.

2. An equilateral triangle has a perimeter of 45cm. What is the length of each side?

   _____ cm

3. Look at the following shapes and match each to the correct description.

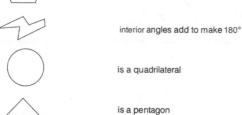

   has no lines of symmetry

   not a polygon

   interior angles add to make 180°

   is a quadrilateral

   is a pentagon

4. In the grid below complete the drawing to make an irregular quadrilateral.

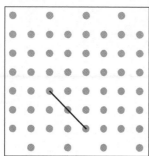

5. Look at shape A, B, C, D on the right.

   a) How many pairs of parallel sides
   are there?   _____

   b) What is the name of the shape?   _____

6. Tick the shapes below which have any parallel sides.

7. Tick the two shapes below which have lines of symmetry.

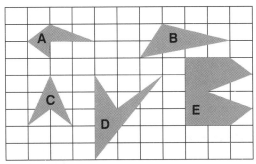

8. How many equilateral triangles with a base of 5cm can be fitted into this regular hexagon?

_____

9. Looking at the kite on the right, circle the letters of the statements which are correct.

A Another name for this shape is a quadrilateral.

B The opposite angles are equal.

C This shape has two lines of symmetry.

D The diagonals are perpendicular to each other.

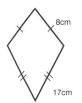

10. Angle $c = 90°$ and angle $b = 60°$, so what is angle a?

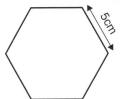

angle $a =$ _____°

/10

43

Test 21: 3-D shapes

1. How many **faces** do the following 3-D shapes have?

   a) Cube   _____

   b) Cylinder   _____

   c) Sphere   _____

2. How many **edges** do the following 3-D shapes have?

   a) Cuboid   _____

   b) Cone   _____

   c) Square-based pyramid   _____

3. How many **vertices** do the following 3-D shapes have?

   a) Cylinder   _____

   b) Cube   _____

   c) Triangular-based pyramid   _____

4. Which two of the following are correct nets for a cuboid?

B

A

C   D   _____ and _____

5. Which 3-D shape has four vertices and four faces?

   _____

Jamie has built the shape on the right out of straws.

6. He uses the straw house to work out the properties of the shape.

    a) How many triangular faces are there? _____

    b) How many square faces are there? _____

    c) How many vertices are there? _____

7. If Jamie decides to make a new model of the same shape and uses a new straw for each edge, how many straws are needed altogether?

    _____ straws

8. Denzel and Pradeep are playing a guessing game. They take it in turns to describe a shape and guess what the shape is. See if you can guess the shapes the boys are describing.

    The shape I am thinking of has...

    a) six triangular faces, one hexagonal face, seven vertices and twelve edges.

    _____

    b) one curved face and two circular faces. It has two edges and no vertices.

    _____

    c) three rectangular faces, two triangular faces, nine edges and six vertices.

    _____

9. Name two common 3-D shapes that do not have vertices.

    _____   _____

10. What type of pyramid has the same number of faces as a triangular prism?

    _____

/10

1. Join the angles up to the correct labels.

reflex angle

acute angle

right angle

obtuse angle

2. Estimate the size of the acute angles below. (Do not use a protractor.)

$x =$ _____ ° $y =$ _____ °

3. Estimate the size of the obtuse angles below. (Do not use a protractor.)

$a =$ _____ ° $b =$ _____ °

4. Look at the parallelogram below and calculate the angle x. (Do not use a protractor.)

70° $x°$

$x =$ _____ °

5. Calculate the angle x in the isosceles triangle below. (Do not use a protractor.)

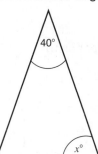

40°

$x°$

$x =$ _____ °

6. Measure accurately the angle marked x below. Use a protractor.

$x =$ _____ °

7. Measure accurately the angle marked z below. Use a protractor.

$z =$ _____ °

8. Measure all the angles in this triangle. Use a protractor.

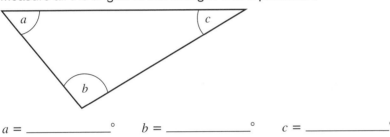

$a =$ _____ ° $b =$ _____ ° $c =$ _____ °

9. Measure accurately the angle marked y below. Use a protractor.

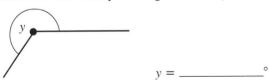

$y =$ _____ °

10. Measure accurately the angles marked s and t below. Use a protractor.

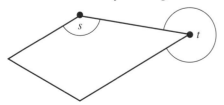

$s =$ _____ ° $t =$ _____ °

/10

Test 23: Perimeter, area and volume

1. What is the perimeter of the shape below?

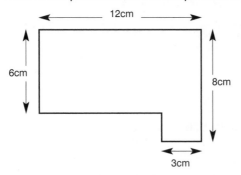

_____ cm

2. Look at the shape on the cm square grid.

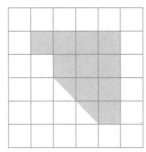

What is the area of this shape?

_____ cm²

3. A regular pentagon has a perimeter of 32cm.

What is the length of each side of the pentagon? _____ cm

4. What is the area of this football pitch?

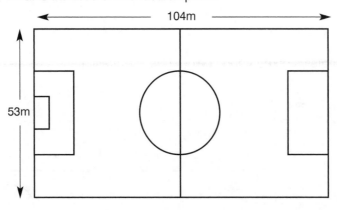

_____ m²

5. Tick the two shapes below which have the same area.

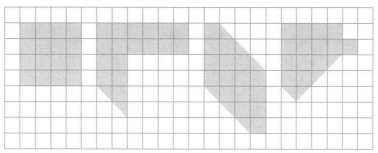

6. What is the area of the isosceles triangle on the right? _____ cm²

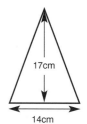

17cm

14cm

7. What is the surface area of this cuboid?

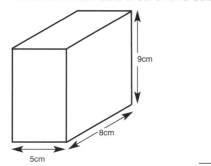

9cm

8cm

5cm

_____ cm²

8. What is the volume of this open-top tank?

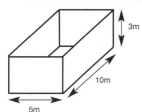

3m

10m

5m

_____ m³

9. A cube has a volume of 1000cm³. What is the area of each face?

_____ cm²

10. What is the volume of a cube with an edge that measures 7cm?

_____ cm³

/10

1. Write down the coordinates of points A, B, C and D

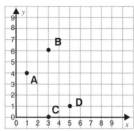

A = (,)   B = (,)

C = (,)   D = (,)

2. Write down the coordinates of points A, B, C and D.

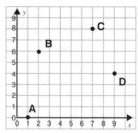

A = (,)   B = (,)

C = (,)   D = (,)

3. Points A, B, C and D make a rectangle. Plot the missing point D on the grid and complete the rectangle.

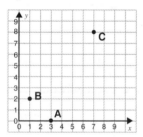

4. Write down the coordinates of points P, Q, R and S.

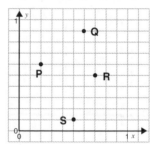

P = (,)   Q = (,)

R = (,)   S = (,)

5. Write down the coordinates of points B, C, D and E.

B = (,)   C = (,)

D = (,)   E = (,)

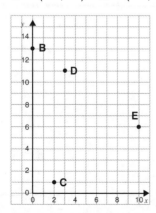

6. Plot points J, K, L and M on the grid below.

J (1, 7)   K (6, 5)

L (9, 13)   M (4, 10)

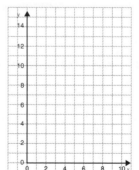

7. This chart represents the locations of various places in Octford.

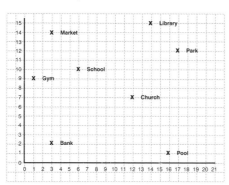

a) What are the coordinates of the park?

_____

b) What are the coordinates of the market?

_____

c) What are the coordinates of the pool?

_____

8. Write down the coordinates of points M, N, O and P.

M = (,)   N = (,)

O = (,)   P = (,)

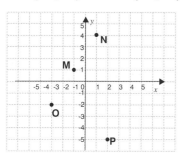

9. Plot point M on the grid below to complete the square JKLM.

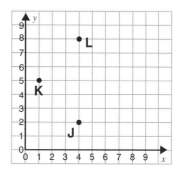

10. Plot point D on the grid below and complete the rectangle ABCD.

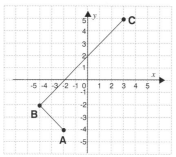

/10

Test 25: Reflection, translation and rotation

1. Using a ruler, complete the diagram below to make a symmetrical shape.

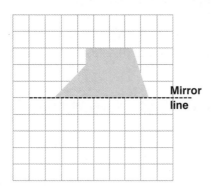

2. Using a ruler, draw the reflection of this shape.

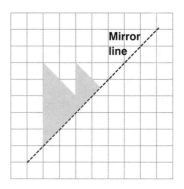

3. Which of these letters are symmetrical?

F   H   B   J

_____ and _____

4. Look at the shape in the diagram below. Write the letter of the shape that would be its reflection.

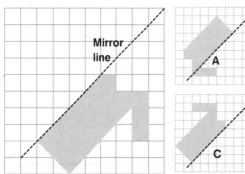

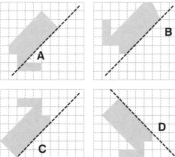

Letter

_____

5. Make this pattern symmetrical about the central line by adding four shaded blocks.

6. Using a ruler, draw the shape below rotated 90° in a *clockwise* direction about point B.

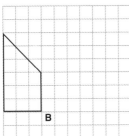

7. Using a ruler, draw the shape below rotated 180° in a *clockwise* direction about point D.

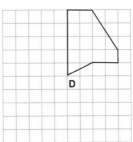

8. Using a ruler, draw the shape below rotated 90° in an *anti-clockwise* direction about point E.

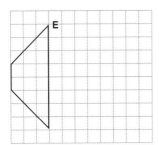

9. Using a ruler, draw the shape below rotated 180° in an *anti-clockwise* direction about point A.

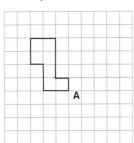

10. Using a ruler, draw the shape on the right, translating it three squares to the right and two squares upwards.

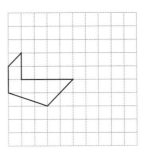

/10

Test 26: Length, capacity and weight

1. Convert these units of length.

   a) 3m = _____ cm

   b) 45mm = _____ cm

   c) 3.5km = _____ m

2. Convert these units of weight.

   a) 3500g = _____ kg

   b) 750kg = _____ tonnes

   c) 4.06kg = _____ g

3. Convert these units of capacity.

   a) 3.5cl = _____ ml

   b) 3450ml = _____ litres

   c) 9.052 litres = _____ ml

4. Write an approximate imperial measurement for each of the following.

   a) 1kg = _____ pounds

   b) 1m = _____ inches

   c) 9 litres = _____ gallons

5. How much water is in this jug?

3 litres

2 litres

1 litre

_____ litres

6. Measure the lengths of these three lines with your ruler.

    a) _____   _____

    b) _____   _____

    c) _____   _____

7. How much more flour do you need to add to these kitchen scales to make 1.8kg?

    _____ kg

8. When opened, a tap lets 100ml of water through every second.

    How much water passes through the open tap in 2.5 minutes?

    _____ ml

9. A man walks 1.4km to work every day and at the end of the day walks back home again. How many kilometres does the man walk in a normal five-day working week?

    _____ km

10. Write down the readings on these three thermometers.

    a) _____ °C   b) _____ °C   c) _____ °C

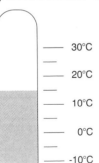
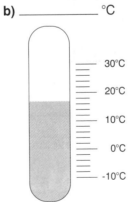
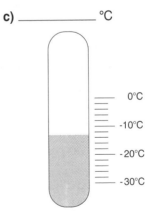

/10

1. What fraction of 3 hours is 30 minutes?

$$\frac{\square}{\square}$$

2. How many seconds are there in 45 minutes?

_____ seconds

3. Jon sets out from school at 3:30pm. He then goes to see his grandma and eventually gets home at 19:45. How many minutes after he left school did he arrive home?

_____ min

4. How many minutes are there in 24 hours?

_____ min

5. Use this calendar to answer the questions below.

September 2012						
Sun	Mon	Tue	Wed	Thu	Fri	Sat
						1
2	3	4	5	6	7	8
9	10	11	12	13	14	15
16	17	18	19	20	21	22
23	24	25	26	27	28	29
30						

a) School starts on the second Wednesday in September, what date is that?

_____

b) Jack arrives back from holiday on the last Monday in August, what date is that?

_____

6. Billy gets to the cinema at 17:30. The film starts at 18:25.

a) How long must Billy wait before the film starts? _____ min

b) The film lasts for 115 minutes. What time does it finish? _____

7. Sally goes on holiday for 10 days, and she arrives back on the 4th of July 2012.

July 2012						
Sun	Mon	Tue	Wed	Thu	Fri	Sat
1	2	3	4	5	6	7
8	9	10	11	12	13	14
15	16	17	18	19	20	21
22	23	24	25	26	27	28
29	30	31				

What day of the week did Sally leave on? _____

8. What is $\frac{2}{3}$ of 2 hours? _____

9. Sasha can run a kilometre in four minutes and 15 seconds. If Sasha runs at the same speed, how long will it take her to run seven kilometres?

_____ min _____ s

10. James puts on a DVD to watch at twenty-five past five. The DVD finishes at quarter to eight. How many minutes does the DVD last?

_____ min

/10

In Chang's computer game she has to take jewels safely to the wizard's cave and avoid the haunted hazels and goblin's trapdoors along the way.

1. Circle the safest route to the wizard's cave.

   A fd3 L fd3 R fd6

   B fd3 R fd3 L fd3 L fd6 R fd3

   C fd8 L fd3 R fd1

   D fd1 R fd3 L fd6 L fd2 R fd1

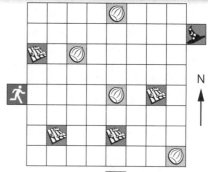

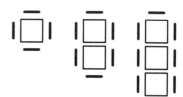

N

Start

Goblin's trapdoors

Haunted hazels

Wizard's cave

2. What is the quickest route if Chang wants to travel to the most southerly haunted hazel?

   _____

3. What is the quickest route to arrive at the most westerly goblin trapdoor?

   _____

4. These diagrams represent the standard ratio of tables to chairs supplied by a conference organisation. What would be the ratio representing the tenth set of tables and chairs in this sequence?

   _____

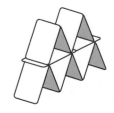

5. Danny knows it will take 15 cards to complete his three-storey card pyramid, but how many cards will he need to build a five-storey card pyramid?

   _____ cards

/5

You will need to complete this test on a blank piece of paper. Find somebody to read these questions out for you. They should read them out twice and then leave 10 seconds before moving on to the next question.

1. Round three thousand nine hundred and fifty to the nearest 100.

2. What are the next two numbers in this sequence?

    one   two   four   eight   sixteen

3. What is the lowest common multiple of five and eight?

4. To the sum of sixteen and twenty-four, add nineteen.

5. What is nineteen less than one thousand and six?

6. What is twenty-one, add, minus sixteen?

7. What is the answer to the calculation twenty times forty?

8. Seb makes six round trips of fifteen kilometres to see his aunt. How many kilometres does he travel in total?

9. Eleven children share three hundred and thirty coloured sweets between them. How many do they get each?

10. If x equal eight, what is the value of six x plus three?

11. What is the sum of one-third of twelve and a quarter of twelve and a half of twelve?

12. What is the equivalent numerical fraction to nought point four in its lowest form?

13. Prices in a sale are reduced by twenty-five percent. If a bike costs one hundred and sixty pounds, what is the sale price?

14. If there are six goldfish and three angel fish in a tank, what is the probability of fishing out a goldfish first? Write your answer as a fraction.

15. How many pairs of parallel sides has an octagon?

16. What do the internal angles of a triangle add up to?

17. How many triangular faces does a pentagonal-based pyramid have?

18. What is the area of a thirty-metre by forty-metre playground?

19. What figure is half way between seventy-five and eighty expressed as a decimal?

20. Write 'twenty-three minutes past midnight' as you would see it in numbers on a digital clock.

/20

Test 1	**Test 2**	**Test 3**	**Test 4**	**Test 5**
/10 %	/10 %	/10 %	/10 %	/10 %
Date _____	Date _____	Date _____	Date _____	Date _____

Test 6	**Test 7**	**Test 8**	**Test 9**	**Test 10**
/10 %	/10 %	/10 %	/10 %	/10 %
Date _____	Date _____	Date _____	Date _____	Date _____

Test 11	**Test 12**	**Test 13**	**Test 14**	**Test 15**
/10 %	/10 %	/10 %	/10 %	/10 %
Date _____	Date _____	Date _____	Date _____	Date _____

Test 16	**Test 17**	**Test 18**	**Test 19**	**Test 20**
/10 %	/10 %	/10 %	/10 %	/10 %
Date _____	Date _____	Date _____	Date _____	Date _____

Test 21	**Test 22**	**Test 23**	**Test 24**	**Test 25**
/10 %	/10 %	/10 %	/10 %	/10 %
Date _____	Date _____	Date _____	Date _____	Date _____

Test 26	**Test 27**	**Test 28**	**Test 29**
/10 %	/10 %	/5 %	/20 %
Date _____	Date _____	Date _____	Date _____

Colour each box with the correct colour to show how many questions you got right.
0%–20% = yellow, 21%–50% = green, 51%–70% = blue, 71%–100% = red
This will help you to monitor your progress.